Piano
Exercises

Selected exercises from past Trinity exams

Published by
Trinity College London
www.trinitycollege.com

Registered in England
Company no. 02683033
Charity no. 1014792

Contents

Foreword

All the exercises in this book were originally created for Trinity College London piano grade exams. They are reproduced here following requests for a collection of the most popular piano exercises from recent syllabuses. Each exercise has been carefully crafted to help develop a particular aspect of piano technique, while also offering a unique musical challenge.

A range of technical aspects are to be found in these exercises. These include:

- finger and wrist strength and flexibility
- fundamental tone production in both *legato* and *staccato*
- more sophisticated tone production with use of arm weight, balance of hands and voicing of chords
- co-ordination of hands in a variety of musical contexts
- co-ordination of hands and feet in the development of good pedal technique.

Each of the exercises has a descriptive title which will hopefully inspire learners to interpret the music imaginatively, as well as providing a springboard for improvisation and other creative work in the lesson. We hope that both teachers and learners will find these exercises a helpful – and most of all a musical – resource for developing secure technical foundations.

Good luck and have fun!

Peter Wild
Associate Chief Examiner

Initial

Pause for Thought, Ludwig and First Thing This Morning all require good
legato finger technique. Listen for a *legato* flow in the phrase line with no gaps
and no overlapping notes. Listen also for precise hand co-ordination in Ludwig.

Pause for Thought – tone, balance and voicing

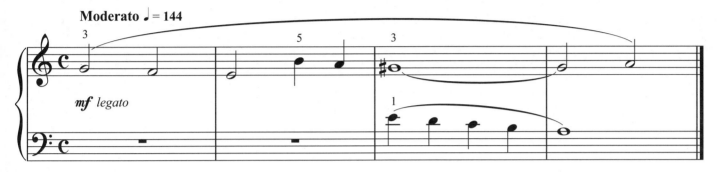

Ludwig – tone, balance and voicing

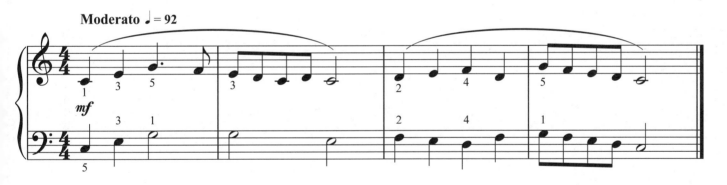

First Thing This Morning – tone, balance and voicing

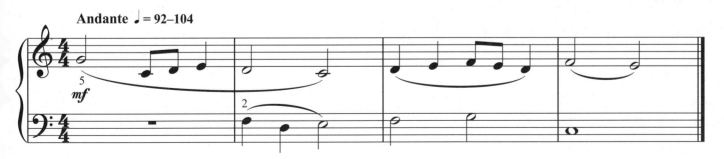

Out in the Sunshine – tone, balance and voicing

Out in the Sunshine requires good *legato* finger technique. Listen for a *legato* flow in each phrase with no gaps and no overlapping notes. Also, be sure to make the dynamic contrast clear.

Bugle Call – co-ordination

Slurring detail is important in **Bugle Call**. Allow the weight of the hand to drop into the first of each two-note slur followed by a light release on the second note.

Here and There – co-ordination

Here and There combines fundamental *legato* technique with neat two-note slurring in bar 5.

Tannoy – finger & wrist strength and flexibility

Tannoy requires spacing of fingers over the five black notes, keeping flexibility in the wrist to ensure freedom of movement.

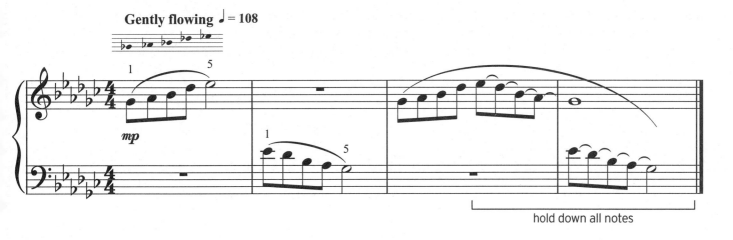

hold down all notes

Relay Race – finger & wrist strength and flexibility

Relay Race requires firm playing. The two notes of each chord need to sound exactly together. Project the *forte* with confidence.

Grade 1

Chinese Lanterns – tone, balance and voicing

Chinese Lanterns features a pentatonic *legato* line requiring careful tone matching throughout the *crescendo* and *diminuendo* detail. Care is needed that the placing of the quaver does not 'bump' the flow of the line. The change from LH to RH should not affect the control of the *crescendo* – it should not be obvious that you are changing hands.

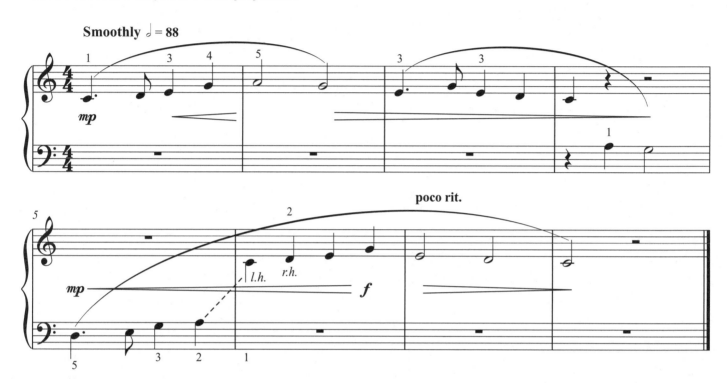

Chickens – co-ordination

Chickens combines *staccato* articulation and slurring detail. Always be precise with articulation – it's an important aspect of the character of the music!

Toast and Jam – tone, balance and voicing

Toast and Jam requires good RH *legato* technique and co-ordinated chord playing in
the LH. Make sure that the placing of the LH chords does not upset the RH *legato*.

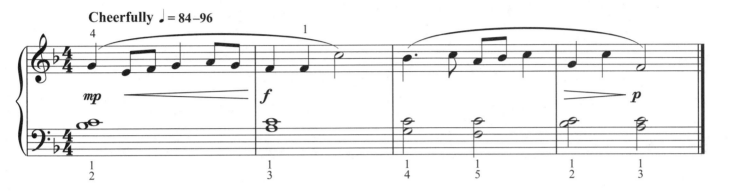

Two at a Time – tone, balance and voicing

Two at a Time moves in short two-bar phrases. The LH has the melody in
bars 1-4 (think of a cello sound) and the RH in bars 5-8 (now a violin sound!).

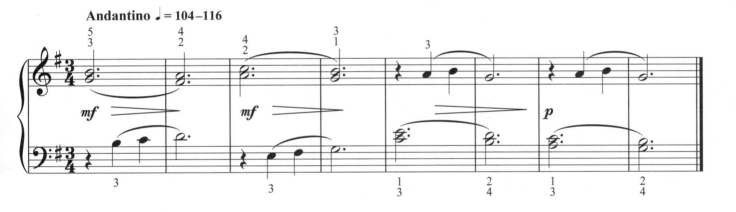

Have Some Fun – co-ordination

Have Some Fun is bright and buoyant in style. Make a clear difference between the *staccato*
articulation and the slurring detail, with both hands coming together in an attractive contrary
motion figure in the last bar. Watch out for the timing of the LH entry in bar 2!

Slithery Snake – finger & wrist strength and flexibility

Slithery Snake requires care and good listening when changing from one hand to the other. The interesting use of semitones makes this a good introduction to chromatic patterns as well as creating a mysterious musical shape.

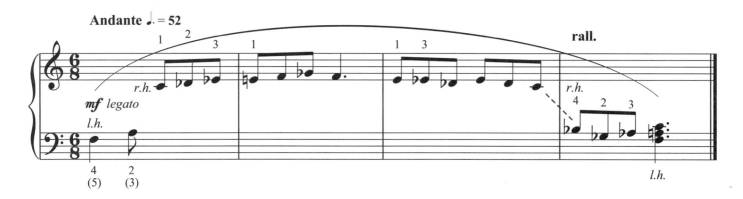

Up and Under – finger & wrist strength and flexibility

Up and Under uses a contrary motion pattern to develop wrist flexibility and hand co-ordination. Avoid a heavy thumb action and observe the contour of the musical shape.

The Hedgehog – co-ordination

The Hedgehog is a lovely duet between RH and LH where the articulation of one hand is copied by the other.

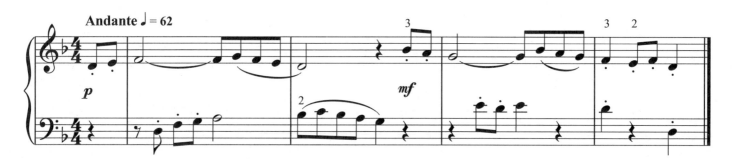

Grade 2

Medieval Mood – tone, balance and voicing

Medieval Mood requires even, controlled finger agility, taking particular care with fingers 4 and 5.
Watch out also for precision of rhythmic placing in the dotted quaver/semiquaver figure.

Up Hill, Down Dale – finger & wrist strength and flexibility

Up Hill, Down Dale has similar patterns to **Medieval Mood** but focuses
on the thumb-under action which is crucial to good scale playing.

Go to the Superstore – co-ordination

Go to the Superstore combines two-note slurs with *staccato* articulation. The syncopated rhythm in the RH of bars 1 and 2 is transferred to the LH in bars 3 and 4. Ensure that the slurring detail is well defined.

Rag Doll – co-ordination

Rag Doll features a different syncopated pattern, imaginatively shared between the hands. Precision in the use of articulation is, once more, important in conveying the musical character.

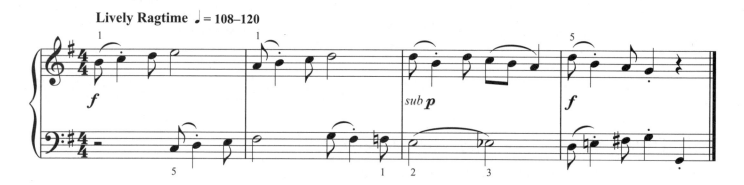

Contrasts in Touch – co-ordination

Contrasts in Touch concerns itself with independence of hands – *staccato* in one hand against a sustained *legato* line in the other.

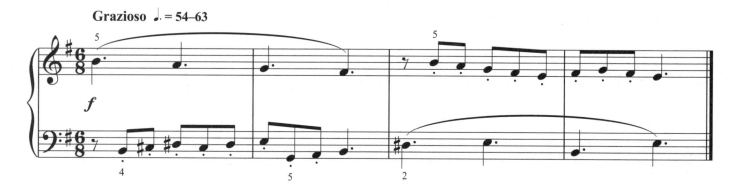

The **Manatee Parade** and **Mountain Echo** are also about hand independence but now in terms of dynamic control. **The Manatee Parade** has a sonorous LH which needs to be sung out like a rising cello phrase. Notice how the dynamic shape mostly matches the pitch shape. The echo effect in **Mountain Echo** needs to be skilfully negotiated. The RH boldly projects the *forte* while the LH plays quietly, as if in the distance. A lot of care is needed with the tone control on the third beat of each bar.

The Manatee Parade – tone, balance and voicing

Mountain Echo – co-ordination

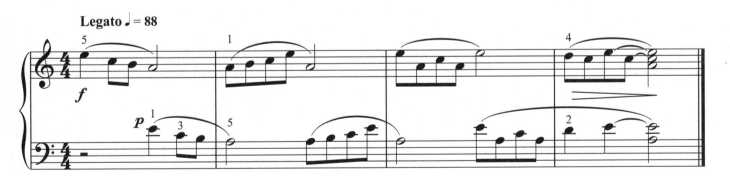

No Reply – tone, balance and voicing

No Reply requires a sensitive balance between the hands. The LH mostly acts as an accompaniment to the RH. On the first line especially, the LH needs to remain in the background so that the RH can sing out the melody line. Notice the lovely *diminuendo* sighing effect in bars 5 and 6.

Grade 3

Weird or What? – tone, balance and voicing

Weird or What? evokes the strange sound world of the Lydian mode (essentially, the major scale with a sharpened 4th). Prepare your hands on the five notes which are used (you will see them in brackets at the beginning of the exercise). Notice how well they suit the natural shape of the hand. Play expressively but observe the use of *staccato* – firstly in the LH of bars 1 and 2 and then in the RH of bars 3 and 4.

Keeping One's Balance – tone, balance and voicing

Keeping One's Balance requires careful hand balance across a range of dynamics. The RH chords are generally kept in the background so that the cello-like melody in the LH can come to the fore. Notice how the expressive phrase shape of the LH matches the rise and fall of the pitch.

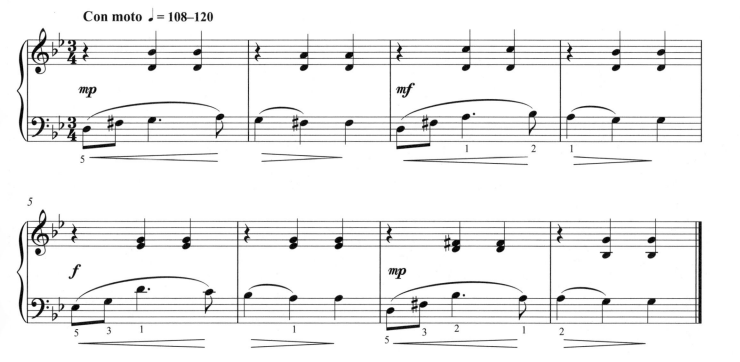

Music Box and Mountain Mists are exercises in using the pedal and crossing hands. The hands never actually play at the same time in these exercises. The pedal change must happen exactly on the beat; co-ordinate your finger and foot otherwise there will be either a gap or an overlap in the sound. Listen carefully – your ears are the best judge!

Music Box – co-ordination

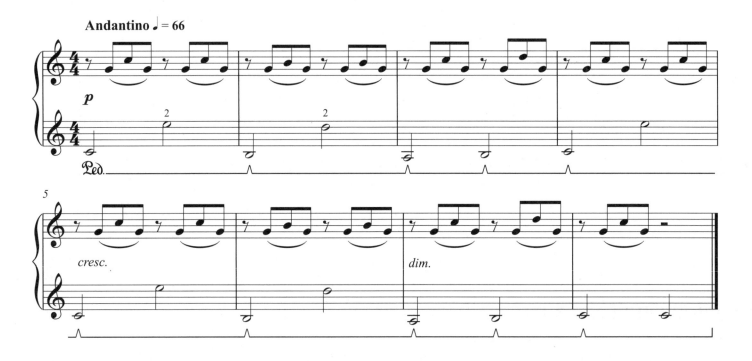

Mountain Mists – co-ordination

Over and Under and **Nimble Jack** are both lively exercises requiring secure finger agility. They are very different in mood but both give ample opportunity to practise crossing fingers over thumb and passing thumb under fingers. Dynamic shape, as always, is important. Notice the *mf/p* indication at the beginning of **Nimble Jack** – here the repeat must be played to accommodate these two contrasting dynamics.

Over and Under – finger & wrist strength and flexibility

Nimble Jack – finger & wrist strength and flexibility

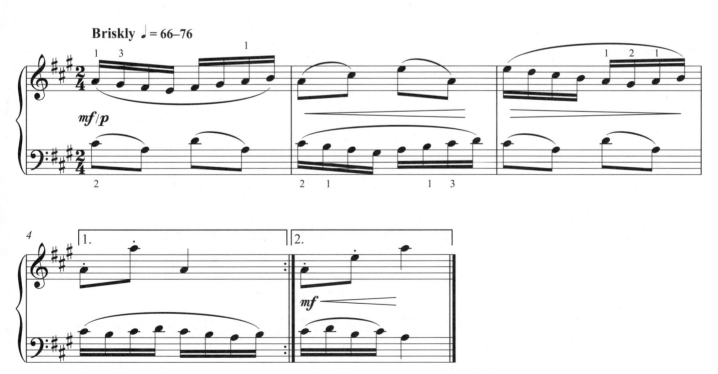

Caribbean Cakewalk – tone, balance and voicing

Caribbean Cakewalk uses jaunty syncopated rhythms while focusing on finger/hand co-ordination. The RH minims should be sustained in bars 1 and 2 under/over the rhythmic figure. Precision in articulation is vital if the character of the music is to emerge. Notice particularly the unexpected stress on the 4th beat of bars 1 and 2.

A Good Work-out – finger & wrist strength and flexibility

A Good Work-out develops flexibility in the wrist. The arpeggio figures require careful placing of the thumb, but notice also the sustained notes (especially RH bars 2 and 3). The finished product should display a strong sense of two beats per bar.

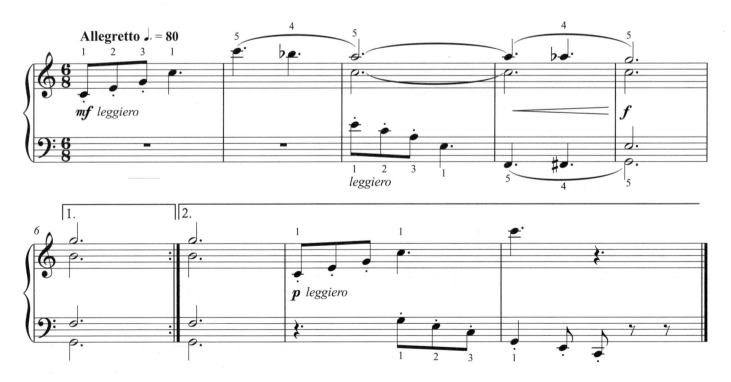

Grade 4

Hustle and Bustle – tone, balance and voicing

Hustle and Bustle requires clarity and evenness in the RH but also a sufficiently supple wrist to enable freedom of movement. The final bar has a fiery demeanour – note the detail in the articulation here.

Go Ahead – finger & wrist strength and flexibility

Go Ahead is excellent for developing wrist freedom. The hands are not required to play simultaneously but both hands get a turn at executing the semiquaver pattern. Notice the placing of the third finger on the third beat of bars 1 and 2, and similarly in bar 3 – some hand extension is required so that fingers are able to play outside the five-finger position. Keep the thumb light and always stick to the same fingering.

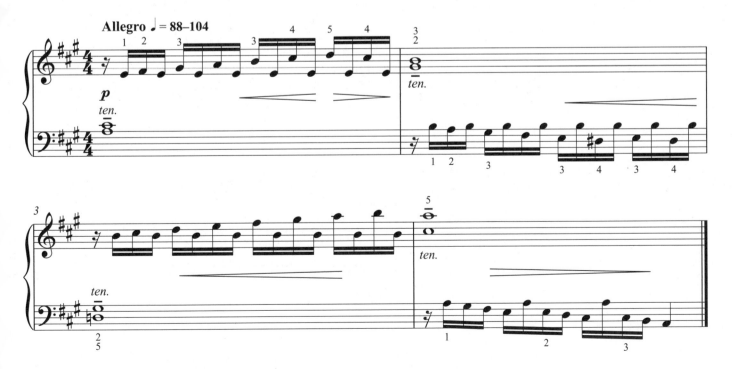

Moving in Closer – finger & wrist strength and flexibility

Moving in Closer offers more opportunity to practise wrist freedom, beginning with an open octave position and gradually closing in the hand. This requires careful finger placing and, once more, a very light placing of the thumb.

Gliding – finger & wrist strength and flexibility

Gliding uses three- and four-note broken chord patterns. Listen for smooth connections between notes, taking care that there is no overlapping. Avoid a heavy placing of the thumb, especially in bars 1 and 2.

Autumn Leaf and **Floating High, Sinking Low** both focus on pedal co-ordination. **Floating High, Sinking Low** uses broken chord/arpeggio variants and needs well-organised fingering (especially on the first line). **Autumn Leaf** creates upward sweeps across the keyboard. The LH needs to move gracefully over the RH, landing delicately on the top note. The pedal sustains the sound so that the LH can prepare immediately for the following bar. Keep the playing exactly rhythmic so that it conforms with the $\frac{6}{8}$ metre. In both exercises the pedal change occurs on the first beat of each bar. The footwork should be precisely co-ordinated and the ears listening carefully for any overlapping or gaps in the sound.

Autumn Leaf – co-ordination

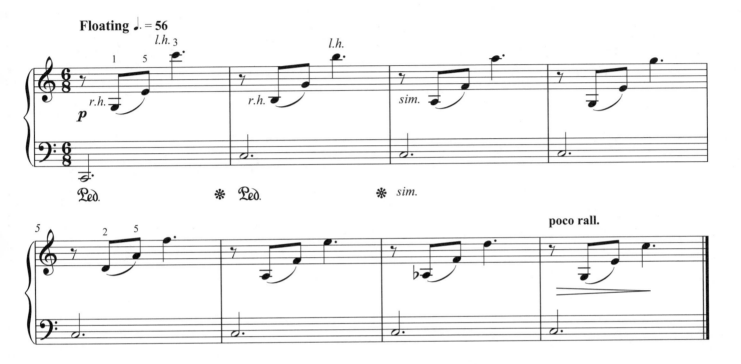

Floating High, Sinking Low – co-ordination

Fun and Games – tone, balance and voicing

The technical focus of **Fun and Games** should be on the management of the RH 3rds, ensuring that the two notes sound simultaneously with evenness of tone. Slurring and *staccato* articulation is required as well as contrasts in dynamic from LH to RH.

Cheeky Charlie – finger & wrist strength and flexibility

The humorous character of **Cheeky Charlie** provides a vehicle for precision in hand co-ordination and articulation. Organisation of fingering is crucial here, and consistency in the use of finger patterns will help to develop accuracy and confidence.

Grade 5

Windmills – tone, balance and voicing

In **Windmills,** the melody line is accompanied by sustained notes, often in the same hand.
The RH requires great flexibility in order to maintain the *legato* line.

Quite Contrary – co-ordination

Quite Contrary reveals a quirky use of contrary motion. The unusual
placing of the thumbs in bar 2 should not affect the *legato*.

Neat and Tidy – finger & wrist strength and flexibility

Neat and Tidy focuses on ornaments. Four different types of ornamental figure are used in the RH. Bar 4 should first of all be practised without the *rit.* to enable clear understanding of the rhythmic subdivisions, which should still be clear when the *rit.* is eventually applied.

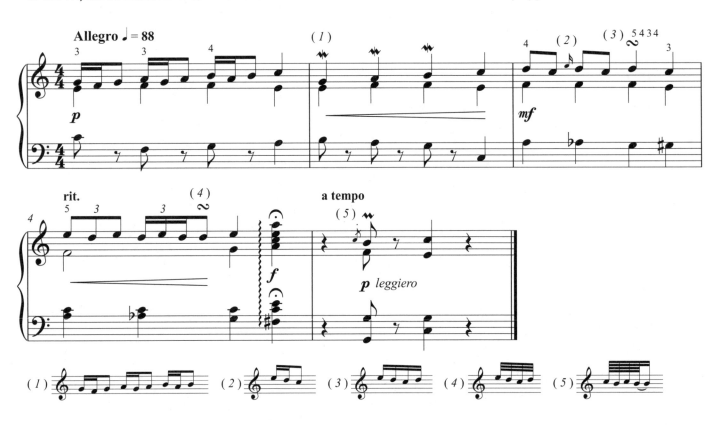

Loops and Leaps – tone, balance and voicing

Loops and Leaps focuses on hand extension and wrist freedom. The key of D♭ gives a different feeling to the hand shape – particularly in the RH where the thumb is often placed on a black note. On the first line, avoid any heavy use of the thumb. The treble clef notes on the second line are split between the hands, and the LH plays the notes with downward pointing stems.

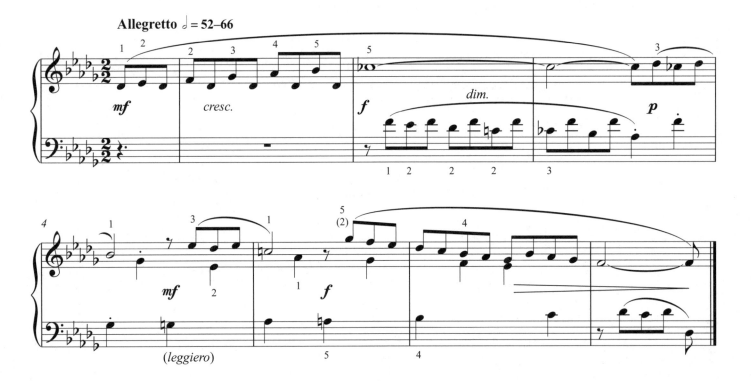

Aperto – co-ordination

In **Aperto** the RH sings out above a more subdued Alberti-style bass in the LH.
Keep the LH wrist loose and take care, particularly in bar 3, that there are no
ugly tonal bumps as the LH negotiates the second and third beats.

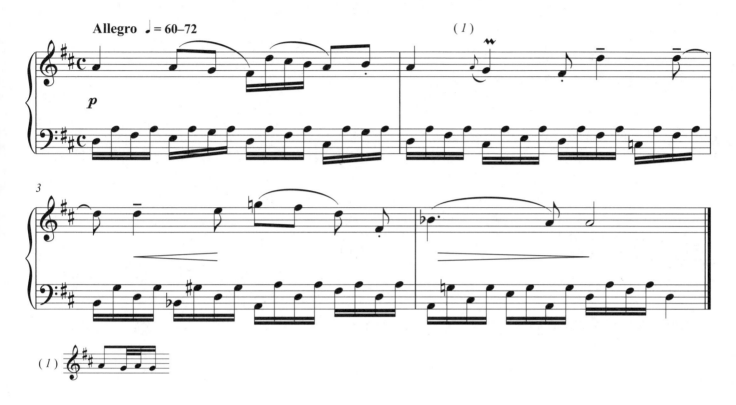

Best Behaviour – co-ordination

Best Behaviour requires good hand balance. Notice the sustained bass line – it is
only necessary to hold each of the dotted crotchets for the length of a crotchet,
which will produce the desired musical effect while allowing the fingers freedom
to move. The RH slurring in bars 3 and 4 should be very elegantly placed.

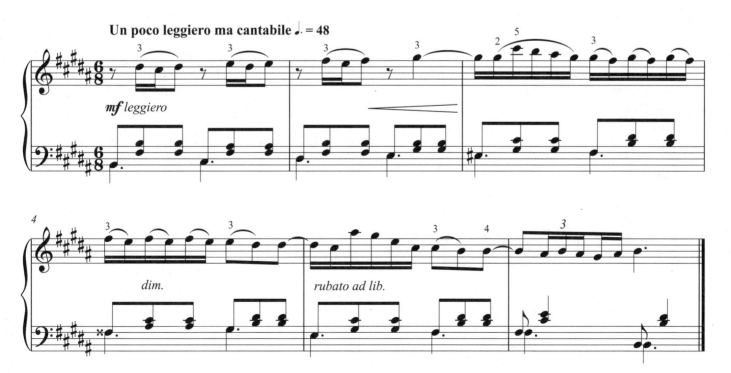

Run and Jump – tone, balance and voicing

Run and Jump is tremendous fun. The right choice of tempo is important for the character to emerge, but the semiquaver work should be clear and evenly placed. Watch out for the fingering in bar 3 and enjoy the quirky use of dynamics in the last two bars.

Lament – finger & wrist strength and flexibility

Lament is deeply expressive. Pedal changes should be at the beginning of each bar and the LH should cross over the RH with a relaxed sweep and a measured placing of the top note. On the second line the *crescendo* needs to be carefully gauged so that there is a gradual build-up of tone towards the *forte*. The intensity of the mood deepens throughout the second half of the exercise.

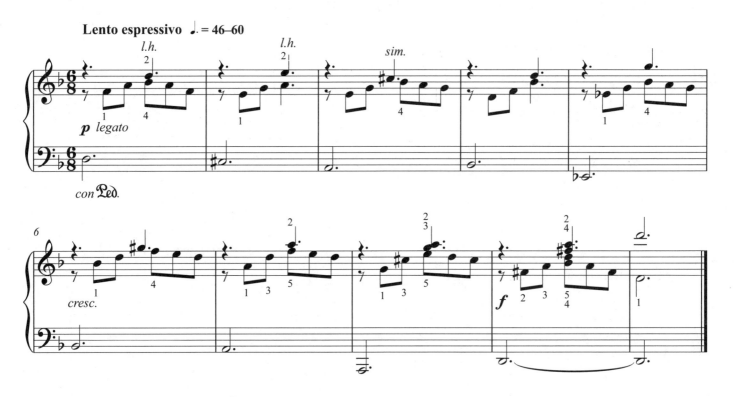

Grade 6

Chromatic Rock – finger & wrist strength and flexibility

Chromatic Rock requires neatness of fingerwork in the RH figures – ideally a well-rounded hand-shape with the thumb placed up near the edge of the black keys. The character of the exercise is complemented by the strong LH gestures – the syncopations need to be confidently accented.

Chameleon – finger & wrist strength and flexibility

Chameleon is a flighty ascent and descent with an unexpected change in the scale pattern halfway through. Dynamic control is enormously important and the whole exercise should be executed with seamless changes of hand. Note the *poco meno mosso*, marked ***pp***, in bar 3. Here the notes of the descending whole-tone scale are sustained in order to evoke a distant, almost magical atmosphere.

sustain all notes with fingers

A Neat Idea – co-ordination

A Neat Idea gives an opportunity to focus on a variety of ornamental figuration.
The LH provides a delicate support with some lightly placed articulation.

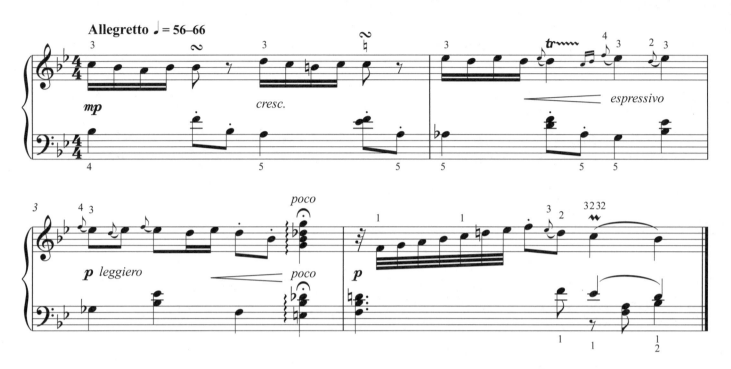

Stubborn – co-ordination

Stubborn is resolute and dramatic. The repeated notes in the RH are insistent and drive
the music forward. Experimenting with alternating fingers on the repeated notes (at
the beginning of the first bar for example, using fingers 3212) can help achieve neat
execution and, indeed, help with the sense of rhythmic stress. The sense of percussive
attack increases through the *crescendo* in the second half of the exercise.

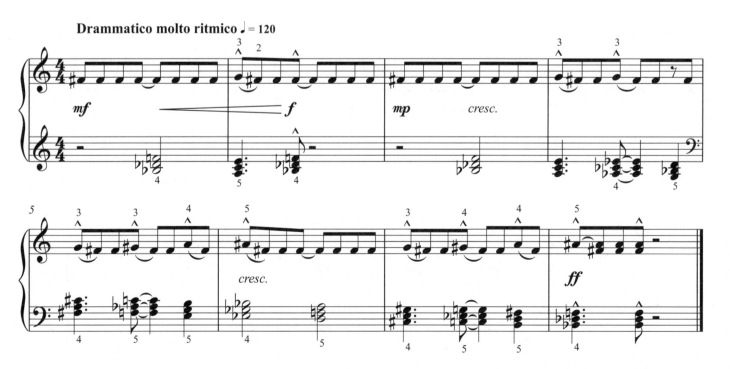

Gladiators – co-ordination

Gladiators also requires a marked percussive attack. Clarity in the articulation of the semiquaver figure is essential – take particular care with the LH on the second line.

Not Quite Sure – co-ordination

Not Quite Sure is a lovely miniature characterisation. A light, neat placing of the acciaccatura is essential, squashing the notes tightly together. The unusual **poco esitando** direction indicates a slightly tentative feeling in the first few bars. This has to be subtle, but one way of handling it is by applying a slight element of holding back at the ends of bars 1 and 2 before hurtling off into the *accelerando* of bar 3. The *tremolando* in bar 4 is a notably dramatic gesture – this can be managed by playing fingers 5, 3 and 2 in both hands simultaneously, alternating with the thumb notes. The wrist needs to be free to allow the effect of the *tremolando* to shimmer.

Sad Story – tone, balance and voicing

The main focus of **Sad Story** is the handling of texture. This exercise offers a classic example of piano writing which requires a *cantabile* melody line, a sustained bass and sympathetically placed quaver figures in the mid texture. Take particular care with the projection of the upper Bb in bar 2 and notice how, in the second half, the melody line descends through the texture – these important notes must not be allowed to get lost within the surrounding activity. Pedalling should coincide with the changes in harmony.

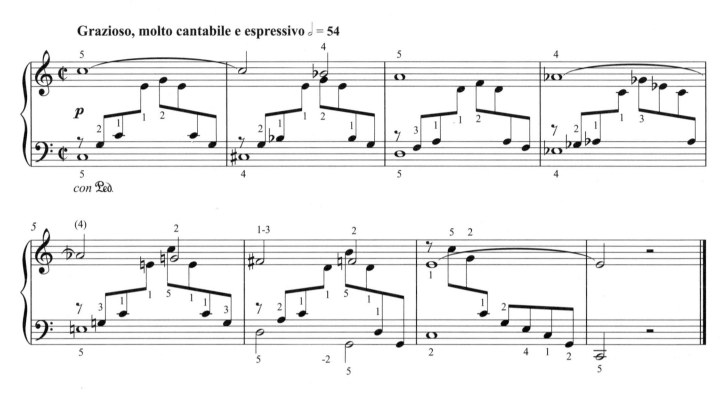

Make it Fit! – tone, balance and voicing

The perennial two-against-three rhythm is given full exposure in **Make it Fit!**.
Try tapping the rhythm with both hands on a hard surface so that you become confident before playing the notes.

28

Grade 7

Puppeteer – co-ordination

Neatness of articulation and agility are keywords in **Puppeteer**. Imagine the puppets bouncing up and down on their strings – this will help make the music sound colourful. The repeat lets you show that your articulation is just as effective whatever dynamic level you are playing at.

A Heavy Heart – finger & wrist strength and flexibility

A Heavy Heart requires a good grasp of the two-against-three pattern already seen in **Make it Fit!**. Play the chord constructions firmly throughout and maintain a strong sense of four even beats in each bar.

Split Personality – tone, balance and voicing

The title of **Split Personality** refers to the bitonal element of the writing. The sometimes unexpected combination of notes, combined with the buoyant articulation, gives a cheeky feeling to the music. The exercise provides a fun way of developing scale technique. Notice how the dynamic increases at the beginning of each scale pattern.

Gavotte – tone, balance and voicing

The elegance and rhythmic balance of **Gavotte** provides a perfect opportunity to focus on precision and delicacy of fingerwork and articulation. The characteristic half-bar anacrusis of this dance style, found at the onset of each phrase, should lead naturally into the next bar.

Basso Sostenuto and Basso Espressivo both require a rich RH *cantabile* accompanied by a sympathetically balanced LH. In **Basso Sostenuto** the successive LH patterns require the hand span to broaden, and the wrist needs to be flexible in order to encompass the ever-widening intervals. From bar 3, the hand needs to be sufficiently flexible to place accurately and comfortably the interval of a 10th. **Basso Espressivo** has similarly wide intervals but now moving at a more leisurely pace, giving the performer greater time to focus on the control of the ornamentation in the RH. The trill in bar 3 may sound more expressive if it were to begin more slowly and then gather speed as it moves towards the 4th beat. The triplets in bar 5 should proceed very evenly – precise rhythmic co-ordination between the hands is essential here. Pedal is required to complete the expressive make-up of both exercises.

Basso Sostenuto – co-ordination

Basso Espressivo – co-ordination

Con Bravura – finger & wrist strength and flexibility

Con Bravura exploits the cross-accentuation which is a result of the juxtaposition of $\frac{6}{8}$ and $\frac{3}{4}$ time signatures. A percussive attack will give bold definition to this style, reminiscent of Bartók. The main beats of each bar should be incisively presented.

Octaves in brackets are optional.

Ever So Slightly Dizzy – finger & wrist strength and flexibility

Ever So Slightly Dizzy is a witty musical characterisation with an emphasis on controlling RH 3rds. The ornamental figuration in the spread chords should be executed lightly but confidently – the emphasis needs to fall on the principal note (the top note) on each occasion.

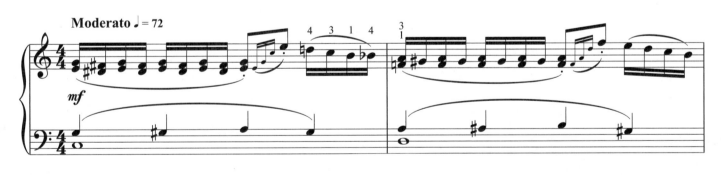

Grade 8

Which way is up? I don't know! – tone, balance and voicing

The essence of **Which way is up? I don't know!** is playing in contrary motion. Accidentals need to be carefully noted so that chord structures are accurate. Also needed is the establishment of practical, consistent fingering. Once the preparation has been done this is tremendous fun to play, breaking out into a quasi-ragtime style in bar 3. Notice how the dynamics are carefully stepped from *p* to *ff*.

Molto legato, commodo – finger & wrist strength and flexibility

Molto legato, commodo has an engaging pensive quality. The tempo should be unhurried, and particular care should be given to the different parts in this four-part texture – the dissonances and resolutions should be identified and listened for in performance. Aim for as much finger *legato* as possible in the management of these long flowing lines. The pedal should not be used – the responsibility lies with the fingers alone!

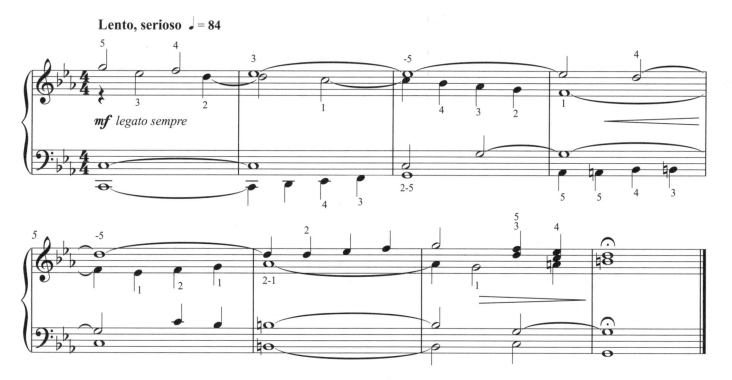

Song of Love – tone, balance and voicing

Balance of texture is paramount in **Song of Love**. The melodic content should be projected with a rich, shapely *cantabile* – note that the use of dynamics is left to the performer's discretion. The lower stave requires a sustained bass line while supplying harmonic detail in the middle of the texture. The lovely chromatic descent in the first two bars is like a subtly placed viola line – a touch of pedal would be admissible in this style, to assist with the *legato* connections.

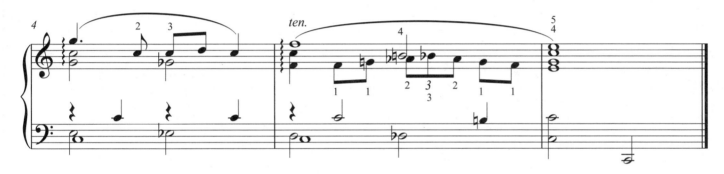

Strutting Your Stuff – co-ordination

Strutting Your Stuff is in real Hollywood mode! The RH rhythms should swing along with flair. Ensure that the triplet work of bar 5 is precisely co-ordinated with the LH. The ending should be slick in its rhythmic placing, starting with a delicate *p* (not easy!) and concluding with an explosive *ff*.

Showtime and Strides are both concerned with the development of octave technique. Octave passages occur with greater frequency in the more advanced repertoire of the 19th century and later. Both exercises are flamboyant and extrovert, needing both technical security and musical confidence. Showtime contains a wide variety of octave patterns – on the beat, syncopated, staggered between the hands and also broken octaves. Strides requires bold calculation of wide leaps – the key of A major provides an opportunity to practise octave placing on a varied distribution of both white and black keys. Practise with care but let your inhibitions go in the finished version!

Showtime – tone, balance and voicing

Strides – finger & wrist strength and flexibility

Two for the Price of Three – co-ordination

Two for the Price of Three – the construction of this is quite straightforward though a high level of concentration will be required in preparation to overcome three distinct technical demands: i) the control of the consecutive 6ths, keeping the hand shape constant but playing with a loose wrist; ii) the co-ordination of the 'two against three' rhythm; and iii) the management of simultaneous *p*/*f* dynamics.

Boisterous – finger & wrist strength and flexibility

Boisterous displays the same ostentatious character as **Showtime** and **Strides**. It sometimes plays around with the natural stresses of different beats of the bar, which makes it great fun to play. Firm placing of the chords is essential, and absolute precision is required in the sounding of the descending 3rds in bars 4-6 and the ascending triads in bar 9. The *staccato* articulation should have a steely cutting edge.